Look and Find®

DISNEY · PIXAR

THE GOOD DINOSAUR

 phoenix international publications, inc.

In a world where dinosaurs *don't* go extinct, they end up becoming farmers! While the crops are being harvested and other important chores are getting done, search the farm for Arlo and his hardworking dino family:

Buck

Poppa

Arlo

Momma

Libby

One day, Arlo accidentally falls into a river and is swept hundreds of miles downstream! Arlo is lost and alone in the wilderness until he sees a familiar critter. Arlo names the critter Spot. While Arlo wanders, look for Spot and these other wild things:

Spot

white bird

this bug

reptile

this gopher

Forrest Woodbush

At first Arlo and Spot are unsure of each other, but soon they're exploring the wilderness together like old friends! As the unlikely pair laugh and play, look for these things that they bond over:

this bug

the moon

acorns

beautiful scenery

these bugs

delicious berries

That night, Arlo begins to miss his family. Then Arlo realizes Spot's parents are gone and he's alone in the world too. While the two new friends make stick figures of their families, look for these fireflies in the sky:

The next day, Arlo and Spot try to find their way back to Arlo's farm, but some mean Pterodactyls chase after them! As a Tyrannosaurus rex family comes to Arlo and Spot's rescue, search for these dinos:

Nash

Ramsey

Thunderclap

Downpour

Butch

Coldfront

Arlo and Spot quickly become friends with the T. rexes. Soon they're helping Butch, Nash, and Ramsey herd longhorns! While they all work to keep the evil Rustlers away, find these longhorns in the crowd:

Just before Arlo and Spot reach the farm, they see a family of humans! Arlo encourages Spot to join them. Arlo is sad to say good-bye to his best friend, but he's glad Spot has a family again. As Arlo reunites with his own family, find these things in the scene:

this butterfly

this footprint

this crop

this butterfly

firewood

human father

Running a farm is a lot of work!
Return to the farm and find these crops and
other things that need tending to:

this animal

this animal

this corncob

this pumpkin

water bucket

feed trough

Wander back to the wilderness and search
for these things Arlo saw:

these berries

Spot's
footprints

this tree

this tree branch

this boulder

this lizard

Skip back to the scenes of Arlo and Spot
becoming friends and find these outdoorsy things:

this bird

this flower

this stick figure

this branch

this butterfly

this tree

Fly back to the fireflies and search around
for these sticks: